AShIKA

Far East
Chinese for Youth

遠東少年中文

Student's Workbook
Level 1

Wei-ling Wu
Hai-lan Tsai

遠東圖書公司印行
The Far East Book Co. Ltd.

Published by

Far East Book Co., Ltd.

66-1 Chungking South Road, Section 1

Taipei, Taiwan

http://www.fareast.com.tw

遠東圖書公司出版印行　版權所有　翻印必究

Distributed by

US International Publishing Inc.

39 West 38th Street

New York, New York 10018

U.S.A.

www.usipusa.com

ISBN 957-612-339-9

Contents

Pronunciation Drill

Practice saying the following tone combinations.

I.
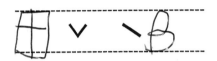

wǒ shì	(I am)
nǐ shì	(you are)
yě shì	(also am / are / is)

II.

| Zhōngguó | (China) |
| Yīngguó | (England) |

III.

Měiguó	(America)
which něiguó	(Which country?)
hǎo rén	(good person)

IV.

| dōu shì | (all are) |
| tā shì | (he is) |

Listening Comprehension

Here are four listening tasks for you. Listen carefully and write in English the nationality of the people mentioned.

Task 1	people	nationality
	I	*wǒ shì něiguó*
	you	*nǐ shì něiguó*
	he	*tā*

Mǐ	people	nationality
Task 3	A	*Chinese*
	B	

Task 2	people	nationality
	I	*měiguó*
	he	*tāshì měiguó*
	we	*wǒmen něiguó*

Task 4	people	nationality
	B	
	they	

-1-

Unit 2   Capsule 1

Structure Reinforcement

I.   Add tone marks to the following according to the meaning given:

we all   american
1. Women dou shi Meiguo ren. (We are all Americans.)

He is also
2. Ta ye shi Meiguo ren ma? (Is he also American?)

II.   How many sentences and questions can you make using "Zhōngguó rén"?

1.   AB _____

2.   CD _____

3.   f | _____

4.   _____

5.   _____

III.   Rewrite the following sentences to include the English meanings given:

He is also English
1. Tā shì Yīngguó rén. (also)

2. Wǒ shì Déguó rén. (not)

3. Nǐmen shì Zhōngguó rén ma? (both)

4. Tāmen bú shì Měiguó rén. (all)

5. Wǒmen shì Fàguó rén. (not ..., either)

Communicative Tasks

Task 1:   In real life, conversations are not only questions and answers. Very often, people give responses to confirm, reject, agree with, disagree with, add to, express opinions and feelings, or ask further questions about what other people say. Study the following model and pay special attention to the purpose of each response.

A: Wáng Lǎoshī shì Zhōngguó rén.

B: (Some possible responses expressing different ideas)

Duì, tā shì Zhōngguó rén.	(Agree with the statement)
Tā bú shì Zhōngguó rén. Tā shì Rìběn rén.	(Disagree with the statement)
Lǐ Lǎoshī yě shì Zhōngguó rén.	(Add to the statement)
Lín Lǎoshī ne?	(Ask a further question)

Task 2:   Answer the following questions according to your real situation:

1. Nǐ shì Rìběn rén ma?   2. Nǐ shì něiguó rén?

3. Tā shì Měiguó rén. Nǐ ne?   4. Nǐmen dōu shì Měiguó rén bú shì?

Task 3:   Finish the following dialogue:

A: Nǐ _shì_ Rìběn rén _ma_ ?   B: Bú shì.

A: Nǐ shì _Zhong_ guó rén?   B: Zhōngguó rén. Nǐ _Bú shì_?

A: _Nǐ shì_ Rìběn rén.

Task 4:   Now you are a new student in a high school in China. A Chinese student is asking you which country you are from. Write down the questions he might ask you.

1. _____

2. _____

3. _____

-3-

Unit 2 Capsule 2

Pronunciation Drill

Practice the following tone combinations. Pay special attention to the changes of the third tone:

I.

xiǎo rén	(mean guy)
Xiǎo Lóng	(Little Dragon)
lǎo rén	(old people)
Lǎo Wáng	(Old Wáng)

II.

Nǐ hǎo!	(Hi!)
Wǒ hěn hǎo.	(I am fine.)
Lǎo Lǐ	(Old Lǐ)
Xiǎo Mǎ	(Little Mǎ)

III.

Zhōngwén	(Chinese language)
Yīngwén	(English language)
huānyíng	(welcome)

IV.

| bú shì | (am / are / is not) |
| bú jiào | (not called) |

Listening Comprehension

Here are two listening tasks for you. Listen carefully and finish the following:

Task 1

Question A: Who are these two people? Write their surnames in pinyin in the blanks:

he _____   I _____

Task 2

Question B: Who are these two people? Write their surnames in pinyin in the blanks:

man _____   woman _____

Structure Reinforcement

I.   Write Chinese for the following:

Chinese name _____   English name _Yingwo_

my name   his name

my Chinese name   his English name

what name   their names

II.   Fill in the blanks to make the following questions meaningful:

1. Nín _____ xìng? (What's your surname?)

2. Nǐ jiào _____? (What's your name?)

3. _____ Zhong _____ jiào shénme? (What's your Chinese name?)

4. Nǐ de Zhōngwén lǎoshī _____?

    (What's your Chinese teacher's surname?)

5. Tā _____ shénme míngzi? (What's his name?)

III.   Read the last conversation in Capsule 2 and finish the following:

Dominic Meyer shì _____ rén. Tā _____ Zhōngguó rén.

Tā _____ Zhōngwén míngzi _____ Mǎ Dàmíng.

Tā zài (is in) _____ xué (study) _____.

Unit 2 Capsule 2

Communicative Tasks

Task 1:   Give responses to the statement given: (In Capsule 1, you studied the model which demonstrated different responses to a statement. Now try your own and see how many different responses you can give.)

A: Wǒde Zhōngwén lǎoshī xìng Wáng.

B: _____   _____

_____   _____

Task 2:   There are 100 Chinese surnames in Chinese. How many have you learned? Write down all the surnames you know.

_____   _____   _____   _____   _____

_____   _____   _____   _____   _____

Task 3:   Look at the following Chinese names. Circle the surnames and underline the first names:

陳　華　　　　　張小鶯

周淑珍　　　　　王　文

Task 4:   Fill in the circled items in the following form:

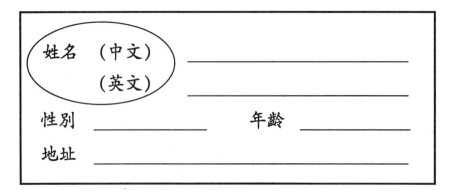

Pronunciation Drill

Practice saying the following tone combinations.

I.

shéi shì   (who is...)
shéi jiào   (who is called...)

II.

qǐng zuò   (Sit down, please.)
qǐng wèn   (May I ask?)

III.

tā lái   (he / she comes)
Yīngguó   (England)

IV.

zhè shì   (this is)
nà shì   (that is)

Listening Comprehension

Here are two listening tasks for you. Listen carefully and answer the questions in English.

Task 1

    Question A: Which teacher is Chinese?

    _____

    Question B: Which teacher teaches Chinese?

    _____

Task 2

    Question A: Who is taking Chinese?

    _____ and _____

    Question B: Who is not taking Chinese?

    _____

Unit 2 Capsule 3

Structure Reinforcement

I.   Write Chinese for the following:

Teacher Wang   Chinese teacher

teacher of the Chinese language   elementary school teacher

my teacher   my friend's teacher

male teacher   female teacher

good teacher   old teacher

II.   Answer the following questions according to your real situation:

1. Nǐ shì dà xuésheng ma?

2. Nǐ shì zhōng xuésheng ma?

3. Nǐ shì bú shì hǎo xuésheng?

4. Shéi shì nǐde hǎo péngyou?

5. Shéi shì nǐde Zhōngwén lǎoshī?

6. Nǐ de Zhōngwén lǎoshī shì bú shì xīn lǎoshī?

Communicative Tasks

Task 1:   Give responses to the statement:

A: Dàmíng shì wǒde tóngxué.

B: _____   _____

_____   _____

Task 2:   In the frame below, draw a picture of someone you know. Then finish the following paragraph. Be sure to tell about the relationships between people.

Zhè shì _____.

Tā shì _____.

Tā yě shì _____.

Tā shì _____ rén.

Tā shì _____ xuésheng.

_____
xìngmíng

Task 3:   What should Xiao Wang say in the following situations?

1. Xiao Wang is introducing his girl friend, who is also his classmate, to his mother.

2. Xiao Wang wants to find out who Ma Daming is.

3. Xiao Wang is pointing at a boy in a photo. He wants to know who he is.

4. Xiao Wang is telling his mother that Ma Daming is his new friend and he is an American.

Unit 2 Capsule 4

Pronunciation Drill

Practice saying the following tone combinations.

I. ˇ ˇ

xiǎojiě	(miss)
hǎojiǔ	(long time)
nǐ hǎo	(hi)
hěn hǎo	(very good)
wǒ hěn hǎo	(I am fine.)
wǒ yě hěn hǎo	(I am also fine.)

II. ... + unstressed

tàitai	(Mrs., wife)
xièxie	(thanks)
yéye	(grandfather)
bóbo	(uncle)

Listening Comprehension

Here are two listening tasks for you. Listen carefully and answer the questions in English.

Task 1

Question A: Which two people are greeting each other?

_____

Question B: How is Xiao Long's father?

_____

Task 2

Question A: Who is Ma Daming's good friend? Mr. Wang or Mrs. Wang?

_____

Question B: How many people are mentioned here?

_____

Structure Reinforcement

I.   Tell when to use the following titles by checking the appropriate boxes. For each title you may check more than one box. If a title can be used for male or female, you may check both boxes.

Title	male	female	elderly	adult	young	formal	informal
xiānsheng							
tàitai							
xiǎojiě							
Wáng Lǎoshī							
Lǎo Wáng							
Xiǎo Wáng							
lǎo yéye							
lǎo nǎinai							
lǎo bóbo							
Wáng Bóbo							
Wáng Bómǔ							
Wáng Shūshu							
Wáng Āyí							

II.   Write Chinese for the following:

Chinese friend   little friend

new friend   old friend

girlfriend   boyfriend

good friend   very good friend

my friend   whose friend

Mr. Xie and Mrs. Xie's friend

Unit 2　Capsule 4

Communicative Tasks

Task 1:　　Give responses to the statement:

A:　Wáng Xiānsheng shì lǎoshī.

B:　_____　　_____

　　_____　　_____

Task 2:　　Write a short dialogue for each of the following situations:

1.　A student is greeting his teacher in the hallway.

2.　A little boy is greeting an elderly man in the street.

3.　Two adults, who have not seen each other for a long time, are greeting each other.

4.　Mr. Wang is greeting Mrs. Lin and asking how Mr. Lin is doing.

5.　Ma Daming is greeting his Chinese friend Wang Wei's mother.

6.　A student is greeting a teacher and asking the teacher's surname.

7.　A new student is introducing herself to a teacher, telling the teacher her Chinese name and English name.

8.　A Chinese teacher is greeting a parent, whom she never met before.

Pronunciation Drill

I.
```
-------------------------------        II.   ----------------------------------------
        sì        shí                              sì        shí
-------------------------------              ----------------------------------------
```

sì	(four)	sì shì sì	(4 is 4)
shí	(ten)	shí shì shí	(10 is 10)
shísì	(fourteen)	shísì bú shì sìshí	(14 is not 40)
sìshí	(forty)	sìshí bú shì shísì	(40 is not 14)
sìshisì	(forty-four)	sìshisì shì sìshisì	(44 is 44)

Listening Comprehension

Here are two listening tasks for you. Listen carefully and answer the questions in English.

Task 1

Question A: What is Teacher Wang's house number?

_____

Question B: Did this person get Teacher Wang's house number correctly?

_____

Task 2

Question A: Where would this conversation have taken place?

_____

Question B: What was the relationship between Wang Wei and Mr. Li?

_____

Question C: What happened at the end of this telephone conversation?

_____

Unit 3   Capsule 1

Structure Reinforcement

I.   Write the following in pinyin:

1)   9   _jǔi_

2)   19   _shiju_

3)   29   _eŕ jui_ (shui)

4)   90   _shi jui_

5)   99   _shtuju_

6)   900   _shiJui_

7)   990   _____

8)   999   _____

II.   How many combinations can you make by using the following words. You may use these words more than once:

xué,   dà,   zhōng,   xiǎo,   xuéxiào,   wǒde,   péngyou,   lǎoshī

_____   _____   _____

_____   _____   _____

_____   _____   _____

_____   _____   _____

Also, by using the above words, make the longest phrase you can. Compare with your classmates and see who has the longest phrase.

_____

(I have _____ words in this phrase.)

III.   Finish the following according to the English meaning given:

1.   Nǐ jiā _____ ? (What's your house number?)

2.   _____ jǐ hào ? (What's your school's telephone number?)

3.   _____ , Mǎ Dàmíng _____?
     (Excuse me, what's Ma Daming's telephone number?)

4.   Duìbuqǐ, wǒ _____ de diànhuà hàomǎ.
     (Sorry, I don't know Mr. Li's home telephone number.)

Communicative Tasks

Task 1:   Give responses to the statement.

A: Wǒ bù zhīdào Wáng Lǎoshī jiā de diànhuà hàomǎ.

B: _____   _____

_____   _____

Task 2:

美國新澤西州
普林斯頓中文學校老師

林美美

電話(六〇九)一二三四五六七

What information can you get by reading the name card on the left?

_____

_____

_____

_____

_____

Task 3:

Now create a name card of your own.

Write in Chinese characters and try to provide as much information as possible.

You may write either horizontally or vertically.

Unit 3   Capsule 2

Pronunciation Drill

Practice saying the following tone combinations:

I. ---------------------------------

ˇ   ˋ

----

kěshì	(but)
qǐng zuò	(please sit down)
wǔ hào	(number 5)
jǐ hào	(what number)

II. ---------------------------------------

ˇ + unstressed

----

jǐ ge	(how many)
liǎng ge	(two...)
wǔ ge	(five ...)
wǒde	(my)

Listening Comprehension

Here are two listening tasks for you. Listen carefully and answer the questions in English.

Task 1

Question A: How many people are there in Wang Wei's family? Please name them.

_____

Question B: What do Wang Wei's parents do for a living?

_____

Question C: Who is a professor?

_____

Task 2

Question A: Who is this person?

_____

Question B: What is this person's name?

_____

-16-

Structure Reinforcement

I.　Fill in the measure word "ge" when necessary and write the English meaning:

1. yí _____ gēge

   (_____)

2. wǒde _____ gēge

   (_____)

3. liǎng _____ gēge

   (_____)

4. shéi de _____ gēge

   (_____)

5. hěn duō _____ gēge

   (_____)

6. hěn hǎo de _____ gēge

   (_____)

II.　Rewrite the following sentences to include the English meanings given:

1. Tā yǒu yí ge mèimei.　(only)

2. Tāmen yǒu mèimei.　(all)

3. Wǒ yǒu mèimei.　Tā yǒu mèimei.　(also)

4. Wǒ yǒu mèimei.　Wǒ yǒu dìdi.　(in addition)

5. Wǒ yǒu jiějie.　(do not have)

III.　Answer the following questions according to your real situation:

1. Nǐ jiā yǒu jǐ ge rén?

2. Nǐ jiā yǒu jǐ ge háizi?

3. Nǐ yǒu gēge ma?　(if yes) Nǐ yǒu jǐ ge gēge?

4. Nǐ bàba shì zuò shénme de?

Communicative Tasks

Task 1:   Give responses to the statement given:

A: Wǒ yǒu yí ge gēge.

B: _____   _____

_____   _____

Task 2:   List the top four occupations you would like to do in the future:

_____   _____

_____   _____

Task 3:   Following the model as shown in the section for "gēge," draw and finish the other three sections. Then tell how many children there are in Xiao Wang's family by completing the last line.

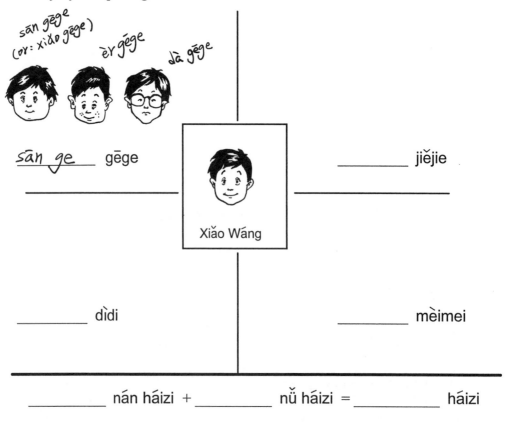

Pronunciation Drill

Practice saying the following tone combinations. Pay special attention to the tone change of the word "bú / bù."

I.

----
bú + ╲
----

bú shì	(am / are / is not)
bú jiào	(not called)
bú huì	(cannot)
bú cuò	(fairly good)
bú bèn	(not stupid)

II.

----
bù + ...
----

bù gāo	(not tall)
bù cōngmíng	(not smart)
bù yán	(not strict)
bù nánkàn	(not ugly)
bù ǎi	(not short)
bù hǎokàn	(not good-looking)

Listening Comprehension

Here are two listening tasks for you. Listen carefully and answer the questions in English.

Task 1

Question A: How old is Xiao Li?

_____

Question B: How old are Xiao Li's parents?

_____

Task 2

Question A: What does Miss Wang's boyfriend look like?

_____

Question B: Why does this girl think her boyfriend is more handsome?

_____

Unit 3   Capsule 3

Structure Reinforcement

I.   Finish the following and then compare the ages of these people:

Wǒ shíyī suì.

Wǒ bàba _____. (38 years old)   Wǒ māma_____. (34 years old)

Wǒ mèimei _____. (8 years old)   Wǒ dìdi _____. (5 years old)

Wǒ bàba bǐ wǒ dà _____.   Wǒ māma ___ wǒ _____.

Wǒ mèimei bǐ wǒ xiǎo _____ .   Wǒ dìdi ___ wǒ _____.

II.   Finish the following according to the English meaning given:

Wǒ bàba _____. (is tall)   Wǒ māma _____. (is really strict)

Wǒ mèimei _____. (is extremely cute) Wǒ dìdi _____. (is the shortest)

Wǒ gēge _____, yě _____. (is tall and good-looking)

Wǒ jiějie yòu _____. (is smart and pretty)

Wǒ _____, _____.(am skinny, but not tall)

III. Draw a picture of someone and write sentences to describe this person:

(Hints: zuì, zhēn, ...jíle, yòu... yòu..., yě, kěshì)

_____

_____

_____

_____

_____

_____

_____

Communicative Tasks

Task 1:   Give responses to the statement:

A: George hěn gāo.

B: _____   _____

_____   _____

Task 2:   Read the following paragraph and answer the questions according to the information in the paragraph:

Wǒ shì Mǎ Dàmíng. Xiǎo Lǐ shì wǒde hǎo péngyou. Wǒ de jiā bǐ Xiǎo Lǐ de jiā dà. Wǒ jiā de rén bù ǎi, kěshì Xiǎo Lǐ jiā de rén dōu bǐ wǒmen gāo. Xiǎo Lǐ jiā de rén hěn cōngmíng. Wǒ jiā de rén yě hěn cōngmíng, kěshì liǎng jiā rén wǒ zuì cōngmíng.

Question A：   Shéi de jiā dà? _____

Question B：   Shéi zuì cōngmíng? _____

Task 3:   Read the following paragraph and draw the figures of the rest of the siblings and tell their ages according to the information given in the paragraph:

Wǒ jiā yǒu sì ge háizi. Wǒ shíwǔ suì. Wǒ yǒu sān ge dìdi. Wǒ de sān ge dìdi dōu bǐ wǒ ǎi. Wǒ de dà dìdi bǐ wǒ xiǎo liǎng suì. Èr dìdi bǐ dà dìdi xiǎo yí suì, kěshì tā bǐ dà dìdi gāo. Sān dìdi zuì xiǎo, yě zuì ǎi. Tā jiǔ suì.

wǒ	dà dìdi	èr dìdi	sān dìdi
15 suì	____ suì	____ suì	____ suì

Unit 3   Capsule 4

Pronunciation Drill

I.
```
--------------------------------
            yī ----- yì
--------------------------------
```

yì tiān	(one day)
yì nián	(one year)
yì bǎi	(one hundred)

II.
```
-------------------------------------------
              yī ---- yì
-------------------------------------------
```

dǒng yì diǎnr	(understand a little)
huì yì diǎnr	(know a little bit)
hǎo yì diǎnr	(a little bit better)
nán yì diǎnr	(a little difficult)

```
--------------------------------
            yī ----- yí
--------------------------------
```

yí ge	(one ...)

Listening Comprehension

Here are two listening tasks for you. Listen carefully and answer the questions in English.

Task 1

Question A: Who can speak French? Who can speak Japanese?

_____

Question B: Who is too old to learn English?

_____

Task 2

Question A: What do Xiao Wang's American classmates think about learning Chinese?

_____

Question B: What is Xiao Wang's father's opinion about learning Chinese?

_____

Structure Reinforcement

I.   Choose a question word from the following to make each of the following questions meaningful:

jǐ suì   jǐ hào   jǐ ge rén
jǐ ge mèimei   jǐ ge háizi   jǐ ge Zhōngwén lǎoshī

1. Nǐ jiā yǒu _____?

2. Nǐ jiā de diànhuà _____?

3. Nǐ dìdi _____?

4. Nǐ yǒu _____?

5. Wáng Lǎoshī yǒu _____?

6. Nǐmen de xuéxiào yǒu _____?

II. Study the "huì" patterns in Key Structure of Capsule 4. Use these patterns to tell about your proficiencies with different languages.

1. Wǒ _____ Yīngwén.

2. Wǒ _____ Zhōngwén.

3. Wǒ _____ Táiwān huà.

4. Wǒ _____ Xībānyá wén.

5. Wǒ _____ Fàwén.

6. Wǒ _____ Rìwén.

7. Wǒ _____ Zhōngguó zì.

III. Tell what languages you want to learn by finishing the following sentence: (Remember that if you want to learn two or more than two languages, you need to use the word "hé")

Wǒ xiǎng xué _____

Unit 3   Capsule 4

Communicative Tasks

Task 1:   Give responses to the statement:

A: Nǐ de Zhōngwén zhēn hǎo.

B: _____   _____

_____   _____

Task 2:   Answer the following questions according to your real situation:

1. Nǐ huì shuō Fàwén ma?

2. Shéi huì shuō Fàwén?

3. Nǐ hěn huì shuō Zhōngwén ma?

4. Nǐ bàba huì bú huì shuō Zhōngwén?

5. Tā xiǎng bù xiǎng xué Zhōngwén? Wèishénme (why)?

Task 3:   The Chinese class is having a discussion. Everyone is telling his / her opinion about learning Chinese. Finish the following by using the words given:

Jane: Shuō Zhōngwén _____ (using "zhēn")

Dave: Xiě Zhōngwén _____ (using "kěshì")

Lily: Shuō "mā, má, mǎ, mà" _____ (using "… jíle")

Tom: Xiě Zhōngguó zì _____ (using "yě")

Hedy: Xué Zhōngwén _____ (using "yòu…yòu")

Eric: Xué Zhōngwén _____ (using "zuì")

Pronunciation Drill

Practice saying the following short sentences:

I.

----
　　　　zhè　　　zhèi

Zhè shì shéi de?

Zhè shì wǒ de.

Zhèi zhāng zhǐ shì shéi de?

Zhèi zhāng zhǐ shì wǒ de.

II.

----
　　　　nà　　　nèi

Nà shì shéi de?

Nà shì tā de.

Nèi zhī bǐ shì shéi de?

Nèi zhī bǐ shì tā de.

Listening Comprehension

Here are two listening tasks for you. Listen carefully and answer the questions in English.

Task 1

Question A:　　How many Chinese books does the boy have?

_____

Question B:　　Who has many Chinese books?

_____

Question C:　　Whose Chinese books are difficult to understand?

_____

Task 2

Question A:　　What kind of dictionaries does Wang Wei have?

_____

Question B:　　How about Wang Wei's friend?

_____

Unit 4   Capsule 1

Structure Reinforcement

I.   Fill in the correct measure word where necessary:

1. yì _____ shū   2. liǎng _____ bǐ

3. zhèi _____ běnzi   4. nèi _____ cídiǎn

5. wǒde _____ Zhōngwén shū   6. shéide _____ bǐ

7. shénme _____ cídiǎn   8. jǐ _____ dà běnzi

9. yì _____ hěn nán dǒng de _____ shū

II.   Help these students finish their statements by choosing "yě", "hái" "zhǐ", or "kěshì."

1. Tom: Wǒ yǒu yì běn Yīng-Hàn cídiǎn.

   Ben: Wǒ _____ yǒu yì běn Yīng-Hàn cídiǎn.

2. Tom: Wǒ yǒu yì běn Yīng-Hàn cídiǎn.

              Wǒ _____ yǒu yì běn Hàn-Yīng cídiǎn.

3. Ben: Wǒ yǒu yì běn Yīng-Hàn cídiǎn, _____ méiyǒu Hàn-Yīng cídiǎn.

              Wǒ _____ yǒu yì běn cídiǎn.

III. Complete the following questions according to the meaning given.

1. Nǐ yǒu _____ ? (How many younger brothers do you have?)

2. _____ yǒu Zhōngwén shū? (Who has Chinese books?)

3. Nǐmen xuéxiào yǒu _____?

   (How many Chinese teachers does your school have?)

4. Nǐmen xuéxiào yǒu _____?

   (How many Chinese students does your school have?)

5. Nǐ yǒu _____? (What dictionary do you have?)

Communicative Tasks

Task 1:   Give responses to the statement:

A: Wǒ yǒu yì běn Yīng-Hàn cídiǎn.

B: _____   _____

_____   _____

Task 2:   Describe the book using the pattern guide:

Zhè shì _____.
(a Chinese book)
Zhè běn shū _____,
(very interesting)
yě _____.
(very useful)
Wǒ bù zhīdào _____.
(whose book this is)
Wǒ xiǎng zhè shì _____.
(my Chinese teacher's book)
Tā yǒu _____.
(many Chinese books)

Task 3:   Now can you describe this dictionary on your own? Try to use the following patterns you have learned: zuì, zhēn, ...jíle, yòu... yòu..., yě, kěshì.

_____

_____

_____

_____

_____

_____

Pronunciation Drill

Practice saying the following short sentences:

I.

... ma?

Hǎo ma?

Dǒng ma?

Xǐhuān ma?

Hǎokàn ma?

Yǒu ma?

Yǒuyòng ma?

II.

... bù ...?   ... méiyǒu ?

Hǎo bù hǎo?

Dǒng bù dǒng?

Xǐ bù xǐhuān?

Hǎo bù hǎokàn?

Yǒu méiyǒu?

Yǒu méiyǒu yòng?

Listening Comprehension

Here are two listening tasks for you. Listen carefully and answer the questions in English.

Task 1

Question A: What does Xiao Li have?

_____

Question B: Which item don't they have?

_____

Task 2

Question A: What kind of notebook did the second person like?

_____

Question B: How many notebooks does he want?

_____

Structure Reinforcement

I.   Complete the word combinations in the following graphic figures: (Pay special attention to the use of measure words and "de.")

shū						
	shū					
duō		shū				
jǐ	xīn	shū				
něi	Zhōng	wén	shū			
liǎng	hěn	xīn		shū		
nèi	hěn	yǒu	yòng		shū	
zhèi	yòu	dà		xīn		shū
yì	hěn		yòng		Zhōng	wén	shū

zhèi		yòu	xīn	yòu		de	máo	bǐ
	nèi		hěn		yòng		máo	bǐ
		liǎng		hěn		de	máo	bǐ
			něi		Zhōng		máo	bǐ
				jǐ		xīn		bǐ
					shéi		máo	bǐ
						wǒ		bǐ
								bǐ
								bǐ

II.   Study the following models and see the differences in meaning with "yào" and "yǒu," and also with "nèi" and "něi."

   Wǒ yào yì zhī bǐ. (I want a pen.)   Wǒ yǒu yì zhī bǐ. (I have a pen.)
   Nèi zhī bǐ shì nǐde. (That pen is yours.)   Něi zhī bǐ shì nǐde? (Which pen is yours?)

Now write Chinese for the following:

1.   I have a Chinese writing pen, but I don't have an ink stone.

2.   I want a piece of paper. Do you have any paper?

3.   Who has a Chinese ink stick?

4.   I want that book. I don't want this book.

5.   Which writing brush is yours?

6.   Which dictionary do you want?

Communicative Tasks

Task 1:   Give responses to the statement given:

A: Wǒ yǒu yì zhī xīn máobǐ.

B: _____   _____

_____   _____

Task 2:   Help Ma Daming: Ma Daming is in Beijing. He is having difficulties with his Chinese. He discovered that his friends gave him unexpected responses to his sentences or questions. Please help him by circling what is wrong with his following sentences:

1. Wǒ yǎo yàntái. (His friend: You bite a Chinese ink stone?!!)

2. Wǒ yǒu yí ge yángtái. (His friend: You have a balcony?!!)

3. Něi běn shū shì shéi de? (His friend: Which book is whose?!!)

Task 3:   Help Ma Daming again. Ma Daming is now in a stationary store in Beijing. For the purpose of learning real world Chinese, he taped his conversation with the shop assistant. When he listens to the tape, he cannot hear some of the shop assistant's words. Could you help Ma Daming to fill in the missing words?

S.A.:   Nǐ yào _____ bǐ?

Ma: Máobǐ.

S.A.:   Hǎo, wǒmen _____ hěn duō máobǐ.

Nǐ yào _____ ?

Ma: Sān zhī. Wǒ hái yào yàntái.

S.A.:   Wǒmen _____ fāng yàntái, _____ yǒu yuán yàntái.

Nǐ yào _____ ge?

Ma: Wǒ yào zhèi ge fāng de.

S.A.:   _____ yàntái hěn hǎo.

Pronunciation Drill

I.
----
xiǎng...
----

xiǎng xué	(want to study)
xiǎng kàn	(want to look)
xiǎng chàng	(want to sing)

...xiě

| xiǎng xiě | (want to write) |
| qǐng xiě | (please write) |

II.
----
qǐng...
----

qǐng shuō	(please say it)
qǐng tīng	(please listen)
qǐng kàn	(please look)
qǐng wèn	(may I ask ...)

Listening Comprehension

Here are two listening tasks for you. Listen carefully and answer the questions in English.

Task 1

Question A: What is Wang Wei doing?

_____

Question B: Who taught Wang Wei to write with a Chinese writing brush?

_____

Question C: What does Wang Wei think about writing with a Chinese writing brush?

_____

Task 2

Question A: What dance can Wang Ying do?

_____

Question B: What dance can't Wang Ying do?

_____

Unit 4 Capsule 3

I. Pattern: Wǒ <u>zài</u> kànshū. (I am reading a book.)

What should you say if you want to tell that …?

1. Teacher Lin is teaching Chinese.

2. Ma Daming is not writing Chinese characters.

3. Students are all learning to sing Chinese songs.

II. Finish the following questions according to the meaning given:

1. Tā zài _____ ? (What is he doing?)

2. Tā zài _____ ? (What is he writing?)

3. Tā zài _____ ? (Is he practicing martial arts?)

4. _____ zài _____ ? (Who is practicing martial arts?)

III. Pattern: <u>Nǐ néng bù néng jiāo wǒ</u> xiě máobǐ zì?

(Can you teach me to do Chinese calligraphy?)

What should you say if you want to ask someone… ?

1. to teach you to sing this Chinese song

2. to teach you to speak Taiwanese

IV. Finish the following sentences according to the meaning given:

1. Wǒ xiǎng _____ . (I want to learn to write that character.)

2. _____ shuō Zhōngwén.

(My father wants to learn to speak Chinese very much.)

3. Wǒ bù zhīdào _____ .

(I do not know whether he can speak Chinese or not.)

4. Wǒ bù zhīdào _____ .

(I did not know that he could speak Chinese.)

Communicative Tasks

Task 1:   Give responses to the statement:

A: Wǒ xiǎng xué gōngfū.

B: _____   _____

_____   _____

Task 2:   Look at the picture and complete the following paragraph:

Zhè _____ Zhōngwén Yī.

Wáng Lǎoshī zài _____.

Xuésheng _____ xué Zhōngwén.

Tāmen huì _____ yì diǎnr Zhōngwén, Tāmen

____ huì xiě yì diǎnr Zhōngguó ____ .

Task 3:   Look at the picture and complete the following paragraph:

Zhè ____ Wáng Bóbo.

Tā _____ liàn gōngfū.

Nà _____ Xiǎo Míng.

Tā _____ kàn Wáng Bóbo liàn gōngfū.

Xiǎo Míng bú huì _____, kěshì tā hěn xiǎng _____ .

Tā shuō, "Wáng Bóbo, nǐ _____ jiāo wǒ liàn gōngfū?"

Wáng Bóbo shuō, "_____, kěshì _____ bù róngyì."

Xiǎo Míng shuō, "Wáng Bóbo, wǒ zhīdào _____, kěshì wǒ _____

hǎo xuésheng."

Unit 4   Capsule 4

Pronunciation Drill

I.

----
        shuōhuà

----
                    huà   huà

Huàjiā zài shuōhuà. (The artist is talking.)

Huàjiā zài huà huà. (The artist is painting.)

Shuō shénme huà? (What language?)

Huà shénme huà? (What painting?)

Zhōngguó huà. (Chinese language.)

Huāniǎo huà. (A flower and bird painting.)

II.

----
        kàn huā

Huàjiā zài kàn huā.   (The artist is looking at a flower.)

Kàn shénme huā?   (What flower?)

Tā huà de huā.   (The flower he painted.)

Listening Comprehension

Here are two listening tasks for you. Listen carefully and answer the questions in English.

Task 1

Question A: Who wants to learn Chinese painting?

_____

Question B: Can the boy do Chinese painting?

_____

Question C: Do you think the boy really knows Chinese painting? Why?

_____

Task 2

Question A: Where would this conversation have taken place?

_____

Question B: What kind of Chinese painting would the man like to see?

_____

Structure Reinforcement

I.   Finish the following according to the English meaning given:

   1. Nǐ xǐhuān _____ ? (Which painting do you like?)

   2. _____ shì shéide? (Whose is this painting?)

   3. Nèi ge huàjiā _____ Zhōngguó guóhuà.

      (That painter is painting a Chinese painting.)

   4. Wǒ xiǎng xué _____.

       (I want to learn to do Chinese painting.)

   5. Nǐ yào _____ ? (How many pictures do you want?)

   6. Nǐmen xuéxiào yǒu _____ xǐhuān huàhuà?

      (How many students in your school like to paint pictures?)

II.   Tell what you like and dislike by using: hěn, zuì, bù, yì diǎnr yě bù.

   1. _____

   2. _____

   3. _____

   4. _____

   5. _____

III.   Pattern: Tā chànggē chàng de zuì hǎo.

      Tell who in your class is the best in …:

   1. speaking Chinese _____

   2. writing Chinese characters _____

   3. painting pictures _____

   4. dancing _____

Unit 4   Capsule 4

Communicative Tasks

Task 1:   Give responses to the statement:

A: Wáng Wěi chànggē chàng de hěn hǎo.

B: _____   _____

     _____   _____

Task 2:   Chinese I students are back from a singing assembly. They are talking about the singing. Their opinions are so different. Some are very positive and some are very negative.

List 3 positive comments they make: List 3 negative comments they make:

Tāmen chàng de _____.   Tāmen chàng de _____.

_____   _____

_____   _____

Task 3:   Ma Daming has learned the following daily expressions:

zàijiàn   qǐng zuò   nǎli, nǎli   míngtiān jiàn
tài hǎo le   tài shǎo le   āiyā   huānyíng nǐ lái ...
zhēn de   zhēn bàng   liǎobuqǐ   nǐ shuō de hǎo
xíng   bù xíng   zāogāo   tài hǎowán le
méi wèntí   Duìbuqǐ, wǒ bù zhīdào

Can you help Ma Daming organize these expressions into categories so it would be easy to learn them?

praise	response to praise	emotional expression	taking leave
for guests	for asking Q.	apologies	OK or not OK

Pronunciation Drill

Practice saying the following tone combinations.

I. ------------------------------   II.   -------------------------------------

      ▬   ▬   ▬   ╱

--------------------------------   -------------------------------------

xīngqī	(week)	xīnnián	(new year)
jīntiān	(today)	jīnnián	(this year)
gāozhōng	(grade 10-12)	dāngrán	(of course)
zāogāo	(how terrible)	Yīngguó	(England)
gōngfū	(martial arts)	Zhōngwén	(Chinese language)

Listening Comprehension

Here are two listening tasks for you. Listen carefully and answer the questions in English.

Task 1

Question A: Why did the boy say "xīnnián hǎo" to the girl?

_____

Question B: Why did the girl say "shēngrì kuàilè" to the boy?

_____

Task 2

Question A: What day is tomorrow?

_____

Question B: What do these two friends plan to do?

_____

Question C: What is the house number mentioned in the dialogue?

_____

Unit 5 Capsule 1

Structure Reinforcement

I.   Create an organizer with Chinese and English to learn the 12 months of a year.

January	yīyuè				

Create an organizer with Chinese and English to learn the 7 days of a week.

Monday				
ASññH				
Sunday				

II.   Write pinyin for the following:

     1) the 5th _____   2) the 15th _____

     3) the 25th _____   4) May 5 _____

     5) May 5, 1995 _____

     6) Friday, May 5, 1995 _____

III.   Answer the following questions according to your real situation:

     1. Jīntiān jǐ hào?

     2. Míngtiān xīngqī jǐ?

     3. Jīnnián shì bú shì yī jiǔ jiǔ bā nián?

     4. Nǐde shēngrì shì jǐ yuè jǐ hào?

     5. Nǐ jīnnián jǐ suì?

     6. Nǐ xīngqī sì qù xuéxiào ma?

     7. Nǐ xīngqī jǐ bú qù xuéxiào?

Communicative Tasks

Task 1:   Give responses to the statement given:

A: Míngtiān shì wǒ de shēngrì.

B: _____   _____

BADc _____   _____

Task 2:   What would you say if you want to invite or ask someone …?
(Hints: …, hǎo ma?   Wǒ xiǎng qǐng nǐ….)

1. to ask someone to come to your home tomorrow
Nǐ_____

2. to ask someone to go to New York with you on Sunday
Wǒmen _____

3. to ask someone to go to practice martial arts with you on Saturday
Wǒmen _____

4. to invite someone to your home on Sunday
Wǒ _____

Task 3:   Look at the two cards below and tell what cards they are.

This is a _____ card.   This is a _____ card.

Unit 5   Capsule 2

Practice saying the following tone combinations.

I.

II.

rìlì	(calendar)	shēngrì	(birthday)
kuàilè	(happy)	sānyuè	(March)
xìngyùn	(lucky)	shēngxiào	(Chinese zodiac)
shàngkè	(have lessons)	gāoxìng	(happy)

Listening Comprehension

Here are two listening tasks for you. Listen carefully and answer the questions in English.

Task 1

Question A: Which grade is the new student in?

_____

Question B: Which grade is Betty in?

_____

Question C: Are the new student's sister and Betty in the same grade?

_____

Task 2

Question A: Are any of the students in China now?

_____

Question B: Will they meet each other in China? Why?

_____

Structure Reinforcement

I.   Complete the organizer for time expressions by filling in the blanks:

past | _____(last year)   _____ (last month) _____ (last week) _____ (yesterday)

present | _____(this year)   _____ (this month) _____ (this week) _____ (today)

future | _____(next year)   _____ (next month) _____ (next week)_____ (tomorrow)

II.   Complete another organizer to help you learn the time expressions:

	year	month	week	day
1	yì nián			
2	liǎng nián			
10	shí nián			

III.   Write Chinese for the following:

1. the year of 1996

2. ten years

3. February

4. two months

5. the 6th

6. six days

7. Tuesday

8. two weeks

9. this month

10. last month

11. next Sunday

12. last Saturday

13. yesterday

14. tomorrow

15. this year

16. next year

Unit 5　Capsule 2

Communicative Tasks

Task 1:　　Give responses to the statement given:

A:　Míngtiān xīngqī liù.

B:　＿＿＿＿＿＿＿＿＿＿＿　＿＿＿＿＿＿＿＿＿＿＿

　　＿＿＿＿＿＿＿＿＿＿＿　＿＿＿＿＿＿＿＿＿＿＿

Task 2:　　Practice with your partner the following dialogue by substituting the underlined words.

A:　Wǒ xià ge yuè yào qù Zhōngguó.

B:　Zhēn de !　Nǐ yào qù duōjiǔ?

A:　Yěxǔ liǎng ge xīngqī.

B:　Zhēn bàng!

Task 3:　　Answer the following questions according to the real situation:

1.　Yì nián yǒu jǐ ge yuè?

2.　Shíyuè yǒu jǐ tiān?

3.　Èryuè yǒu jǐ tiān?

4.　Yí ge xīngqī yǒu jǐ tiān?

5.　Nǐ yí ge xīngqī shàng jǐ tiān kè?

6.　Nǐ xīngqī wǔ shàngkè ma?

7.　Nǐ xīngqī liù shàngkè ma?

8.　Nǐ shì chūyī de xuésheng ma?

9.　Nǐ niàn jǐ niánjí?

10.　Nǐ jīntiān gāoxìng ma?

Pronunciation Drill

Practice saying the following tone combinations.

I.

⌄ ⌄

II.

⌄ ⌄ ⌄

lǎohǔ	(tiger)
xiǎo gǒu	(little dog)
suǒyǐ	(so)
yěxǔ	(perhaps)

xiǎo lǎohǔ	(little tiger)
hěn hǎo dǒng	(easy to understand)
wǒ xiǎng nǐ	(I miss you)
xiǎo lǎoshǔ	(little rat)

Listening Comprehension

Here are two listening tasks for you. Listen carefully and answer the questions in English.

Task 1

Question A: What Chinese zodiac year were they born?

_____

Question B: How did Wang Wei figure out the age of his friend's mom?

_____

Question C: How old are these two people?

_____

Task 2

Question A: How many people in this family were born during the year of the tiger?

_____

Question B: Who is the "old tiger" in this family? Who is the "little tiger"?

_____

Structure Reinforcement

I.   List the 12 zodiac animals according to your personal preference:

1. _____   2. _____   3. _____

4. _____   5. _____   6. _____

7. _____   8. _____   9. _____

10. _____   11. _____   12. _____

II.   Pattern: Wǒ xǐhuān chànggē <u>suǒyǐ</u> wǒ xiǎng xué chàng nèi ge Zhōngguó gē.

What would you say if you want to say …?

1. I like China so I study Chinese.

2. My dog is very cute so I like him very much.

3. I was born in 1984 so my zodiac sign is Rat.

4. He dances very well so we all like to watch him dance.

III.   Pattern: Wǒ <u>shì</u> yī jiǔ bā èr nián <u>shēng de.</u>

Complete the following sentences according to the English meaning given:

1. Tā de xiǎo dìdi shì _____ shēng de. (last November)

2. Tā _____ shì yī jiǔ bā líng nián shēng de. (perhaps)

3. Tā nián _____ . Wǒ xiǎng tā _____ yī jiǔ bā líng nián _____ .
         (grade 10)   (was born)

4. Nǐ shì _____ shēng de? (which year)

5. _____ wǒ shǔ shénme. (do not know)

Communicative Tasks

Task 1:   Give responses to the statement:

A: Wǒ shǔ niú.

B: _____   _____

_____   _____

Task 2:   Answer the following questions according to your real situation:

1. Jīnnián shì shénme nián?

2. Jīnnián shì bú shì niú nián?

3. Nǐ shì něi yì nián shēng de?

4. Nǐ shǔ shénme?

5. Nǐ zhīdào bù zhīdào Wáng Wěi shǔ shénme?

6. Nǐ yǒu gǒu ma?

    (If yes,) Nǐ yǒu jǐ zhī gǒu?

7. Nǐ xǐhuān bù xǐhuān gǒu?

8. Nǐ huì huà lóng ma?

9. Shéi huì huà lóng?

    Tā lóng huà de hǎo bù hǎo?

10. Nǐ xǐhuān bù xǐhuān zhèi zhāng shíèr shēngxiào de huà?

11. Zhèi zhāng shíèr shēngxiào de huà zěnmeyàng?

12. Nǐ yào bú yào zhèi zhāng shíèr shēngxiào de huà?

Unit 5   Capsule 4

Pronunciation Drill

Practice saying the following tone combinations.

I. -------------------------------   II.   ---

⟋ ∨   ∨ ⟋

-------------------------------   ---

yóushuǐ	(swim)	xiǎoxué	(elementary school)
nóngchǎng	(farm)	shuǐniú	(water buffalo)
méiyǒu	(do not have)	shǔnián	(year of the rat)
nán dǒng	(hard to understand)	děng rén	(wait for someone)

Listening Comprehension

Here are two listening tasks for you. Listen carefully and answer the questions in English.

Task 1

Question A: What animal does Wang Wei like the best? Why?

_____

Question B: How about Wang Wei's friend?

_____

Task 2

Question A: Which grade is Li Xiaozhong in?

_____

Question B: What pets does he have?

_____

Question C: Why does he feel unhappy?

_____

Structure Reinforcement

I.   Let's create a zoo, which has the 17 animals you have learned in Chinese. There are 17 circles on this page. Each circle is for one animal. Please be careful when you decide which animal should stay in which circle because some animals do not like each other. For example, "tù" will be scared to live with "hǔ." According to the Chinese tradition, "gǒu" and "jī" will fight all the time. Now use your wisdom and make the best arrangement you can. Also, please give this zoo a name. If you want, you can also add some trees or scenery to make the zoo more interesting.

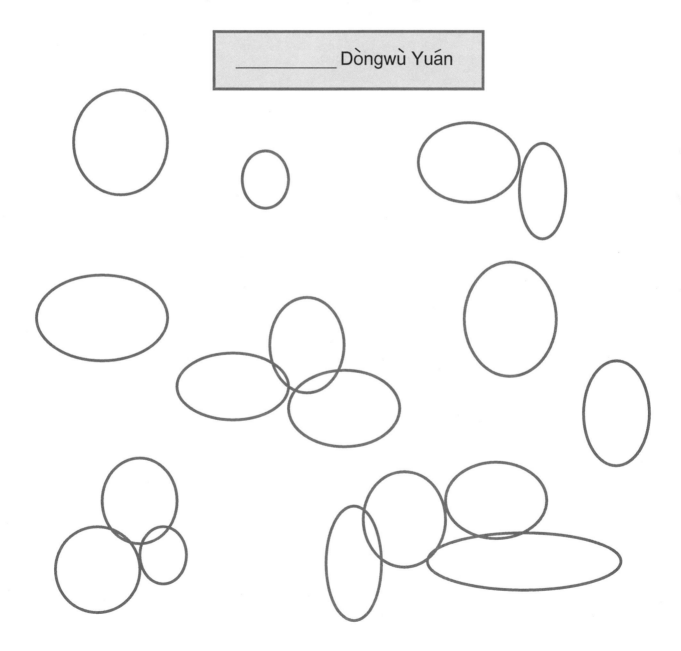

_____ Dòngwù Yuán

Communicative Tasks

Task 1:   Give responses to the statement:

A: Wǒ zuì xǐhuān lǎoshǔ.

B: _____   _____

    _____   _____

Task 2:   Match the statements and responses in the following columns:

Jīntiān shì wǒ de shēngrì.   Zhù nǐ yílù shùnfēng.

Wǒ míngtiān yào qù Zhōngguó.   Děngyiděng.

Zàijiàn.   Nín guòjiǎng le.

Wǒ yǒu yí ge hǎo gēge.   Shēngrì kuàilè.

Nǐ Zhōngwén shuō de zhēn hǎo.   Nǐ zhēn xìngyùn.

Wǒmen xiànzài (now) qù, hǎo ma?   Xīngqī liù jiàn.

Task 3:   Ma Daming is curious about a lot of things about Chinese culture. He wants to ask the following questions in Chinese. How should he say them in Chinese?

1. Why doesn't the dog like the cat?

2. Why do Chinese people have the zodiac signs?

3. Why is the Rat the first (dì yī)?

Task 4:   Answer the following questions according to the real situation:

1. Shénme dòngwù huì fēi?

2. Shénme dòngwù yòu dà yòu pàng?

3. Nǐ zuì xǐhuān shénme dòngwù? Wèishénme?

4. Nǐ zuì bù xǐhuān shénme dòngwù? Wèishénme?

5. Nǐ juéde xiǎo dòngwù hǎowán ma?

Pronunciation Drill

Practice saying the following tone combinations.

I.

yī ---- yì   yī ----- yí

yìbǎi yuán měijīn	($100)
yìqiān yuán měijīn	($1,000)
yíwàn yuán měijīn	($10,000)
yíyì yuán měijīn	($100,000,000)

II.

/ —

xióngmāo	(panda)
zuótiān	(yesterday)
míngtiān	(tomorrow)
xuésheng	(student)

Listening Comprehension

Here are two listening tasks for you. Listen carefully and answer the questions in English.

Task 1

Question A: What did the customer want to buy?

_____

Question B: How much money did he have?

_____

Question C: What did he buy finally? How much did he pay?

_____

Task 2

Question A: What kind of money did Wang Wei's friend have?

_____

Question B: How about Wang Wei?

_____

Unit 6   Capsule 1

Structure Reinforcement

I.   Write in pinyin for the following Chinese money units to indicate how to say them in Chinese:

     1. ¥0.08   2. ¥0.14

     3. ¥0.92   4. ¥1.34

     5. ¥5.04   6. ¥17.00

     7. ¥12.05   8. ¥21.13

     9. ¥136.49   10. ¥408.20

     11. ¥5,800.00   12. ¥34,567.89

II.   Pattern: Zhèi běn běnzi <u>duōshao qián</u>?

     What should you say if you want to ask … ?

     1. How much is this Chinese-English dictionary?

     2. How much is that landscape painting?

     3. How much are these two Chinese writing brushes?

III.   Finish the following according to the English meaning given:

     1. Wáng Xiānsheng _____ . (very rich)

     2. Nèi běn shū _____ . (too expensive)
       Wǒ de qián _____ . (not enough)

     3. Wǒ _____ nèi zhī xiǎo gǒu. (really want to buy)

     4. _____ zhè shì Zhōngguó qián, _____ wǒ māma bù zhīdào
       zhè shì duōshao qián. (because …, so …)

     5. Zhèi liǎng zhī bǐ dōu hěn hǎo. Wǒ bù zhīdào wǒ yào mǎi _____ .
       (which one)

Communicative Tasks

Task 1:   Give responses to the statement:

A: Zhèi zhī máobǐ èrshiwǔ kuài sān máo liù fēn.

B: _____   _____

    _____   _____

Task 2:   These are the reduced sizes of real money. Can you identify them?

What money is it?

_____

How much is it?

_____

What money is it?

_____

How much is it?

_____

What money is it?

_____

How much is it?

_____

Unit 6   Capsule 2

Pronunciation Drill

Practice saying the following tone combinations.

I.   ---------------------------------   II.   --

/   /   / + unstressed

---------------------------------   --

yóutiáo	(fried twist)	mántou	(steamed bread)
niánnián	(every year)	háizi	(child)
rénmín	(people)	shénme	(what)
lái wán	(come for fun)	yéye	(grandpa)

Listening Comprehension

Here are two listening tasks for you. Listen carefully and answer the questions in English.

Task 1

Question A: What kind of beverage was Wang Wei drinking?
Would Ma Daming take the same?

_____

Question B: What was Wang Wei's conclusion about the difference between
Chinese and American? Do you agree with him?

_____

Task 2

Question A: What kind of breakfast did the person want?

_____

Question B: Can you name some items he ordered?

_____

Structure Reinforcement

I. Let's compare a Chinese breakfast with an American breakfast. List all the items you can say in Chinese under each kind of breakfast.

Zhōngguó Zǎofàn   Měiguó Zǎofàn

Drinks   _____ _____   _____ _____

                                        _____ _____

Food   _____ _____   _____ _____

          _____ _____   _____ _____

II. Pattern: Wǒ <u>měi tiān dōu</u> shuō Zhōngwén, kěshì wǒ <u>hěnshǎo</u> xiě Zhōngguó zì.

Now say the following in Chinese:

1. I eat Chinese breakfast every day.

2. My Chinese friend practices martial arts every day.

3. I seldom drink coffee.

III. Pattern: Nǐ chī<u>guo</u> bāozi ma?   Chī<u>guo</u>. (or: <u>Méi</u> chīguo.)

Now say the following in Chinese:

1. Have you ever drunk Chinese soybean milk? Yes, I have.

2. Have you ever been (qù) to China? No, I haven't.

IV. Finish the following sentences:

1. _____ hěn hǎochī.   2. _____ hěn nánchī.

3. _____ hěn hǎohē.   4. _____ hěn nánhē.

5. _____ hěn hǎokàn.   6. _____ hěn nánkàn.

Communicative Tasks

Task 1:   Give responses to the statement given:

A: Wǒ měi tiān dōu hē kāfēi.

B: _____   _____

_____   _____

Task 2:   Answer the following questions according to your real situation.

1. Nǐ měi tiān dōu chī zǎofàn ma?

2. Nǐ měi tiān zǎofàn chī shénme?

3. Nǐ chīguo Zhōngguó zǎofàn ma? Nǐ chīguo yóutiáo ma?

4. Nǐ juéde huǒtuǐ hǎochī bù hǎochī?

5. Nǐ juéde dòujiāng zěnmeyàng?

6. Nǐ hē bù hē kāfēi?

7. Nǐ xǐhuān bù xǐhuān chá? Wèishénme?

Task 3:   Li Long is telling her mother about her new friend Tom, who has just come from America. Fill in the blanks to complete this conversation.

Long: Māma, wǒ yǒu yí _____ xīn péngyou. Tā shì Měiguó _____, shì

shàng xīngqī tiān lái _____guó de.

Mom: Tā jiào _____ míngzi?

Long: Tā _____Tom. Māma, Tom méiyǒu chī_____ Zhōngguó zǎofàn.

Tā bù _____ shénme shì dàbǐng _____ yóutiáo.

Wǒ xiǎng xīngqī tiān _____ tā lái wǒmen _____chī zǎofàn, hǎo _____?

Mom: Hǎo a!

Pronunciation Drill

Practice saying the following tone combinations.

I.

‾ ＼

zhūròu	(pork)
zhīpiào	(check)
zhīdào	(know)
zhōngfàn	(lunch)

II.

ˇ ‾

guǒzhī	(juice)
měi tiān	(every day)
Měijīn	(American money)
hǎixiān	(seafood)

Listening Comprehension

Here are two listening tasks for you. Listen carefully and answer the questions in English:

Task 1

Question A: Who usually does the cooking in Wang Wei's house?

_____

Question B: Can Wang Wei's father cook?

_____

Question C: What does Wang Wei ask his friend to teach him?

_____

Task 2

Question A: What kind of food does the person like? Name some.

_____

Question B: Does he care for chicken or duck?

_____

Unit 6   Capsule 3

Structure Reinforcement

I.   Now you are opening a new Chinese grocery store. There are three shelves in your store and each shelf has six open containers to hold six different items. Label each container to show the best arrangement of the store. (Be careful that you do not put certain items next to each other. For example, it is not proper to put "tea" next to "fish.")

II.   Pattern: Nǐ xǐhuān zhèi běn shū <u>háishì</u> nèi běn shū?
　　　　　　　 Zhèi běn shū hé nèi běn shū wǒ dōu xǐhuān.
　　　　　　　 Zhèi liǎng běn shū wǒ dōu xǐhuān.

Now can you say the following in Chinese?

1.   Do you like fish or shrimp?   I like fish and shrimp.

2.   Do you like this painting or that painting?   I like both of these two paintings.

3.   Does Chinese food or American food taste good?
     Chinese food and American food are both delicious.

III.   Fill in the blanks with one of the "...fàn" combinations in Building Blocks of Capsule 3.

1.   Wǒ gēge hěn huì _____, kěshì wǒ zhǐ huì _____.

2.   Wǒ juéde wǒmen xuéxiào de _____ hěn bù hǎochī.

IV.   Fill in the blanks with one of the "...cài" combinations in Building Blocks of Capsule 3.

1.   Wǒ jiā méiyǒu cài le, suǒyǐ wǒ māma yào qù _____.

2.   Nǐ xǐhuān _____?

Communicative Tasks

Task 1:   Give responses to the statement:

A: Wǒ māma zuò fàn zuò de hěn hǎo.

B: _____   _____

_____   _____

Task 2:   Answer the following questions according to your real situation.

1. Nǐ xǐhuān chī Zhōngguó fàn ma?

2. Nǐ chīguo báicài dòufu ma?

3. Nǐ juéde báifàn hǎochī háishì chǎofàn hǎochī?

4. Nǐ jiā shéi zuò fàn?

5. Nǐ māma zuò fàn zuò de hǎo bù hǎo?

6. Nǐ xǐhuān bù xǐhuān zuò fàn?

7. Nǐ huì bú huì zuò Zhōngguó fàn?

8. Zuò Zhōngguó fàn róngyì bù róngyì?

Task 3:   Students in Chinese I are commenting on the food in the school cafeteria. Tom is
the first one to speak.   Imagine how many more different opinions you can hear.
(Hints: Try to use: zhēn, zhème, …jí le, yòu… yòu…, kěshì, yě)

Tom: <u>Xuéxiào de fàn hěn hǎochī.</u>   Lily: _____

Eric: _____   Jane: _____

Bill: _____   Beth: _____

Hedy: _____

Mike: _____

Unit 6   Capsule 4

Pronunciation Drill

Practice saying the following tone combinations.

I.   ----------------------------------   II.   ---
         ▬ + unstressed   ∨   ╲
      ----------------------------------   ---

chāzi	(fork)	qǐng yòng	(enjoy the food)
dāozi	(knife)	qǐng kè	(give treat)
bēizi	(cup)	hěn è	(very hungry)
bāozi	(steamed bun)	kělè	(cola)

Listening Comprehension

Here are two listening tasks for you. Listen carefully and answer the questions in English.

Task 1

Question A: Where could this conversation have taken place?

_____

Question B: How was "Mápó Dòufu" described in the conversation?

_____

Question C: What other dishes were ordered?

_____

Task 2

Question A: Did Wang Wei feel hungry at the beginning?

_____

Question B: What made him change his mind?

_____

Structure Reinforcement

I.   Fill in the correct measure word when necessary:

1. yí _____ wǎn   2. liǎng _____ cānjīnzhǐ

3. zhèi _____ pánzi   4. nèi _____ càidān

5. wǔ _____ bēizi   6. yì _____ kuàizi

7. jǐ _____ chāzi   8. sì _____ dāozi

II.   Pattern: <u>Wǒmen qù</u> chīfàn <u>ba</u>.

Now can you say the following in Chinese?

1. Let's go and sing.   2. Let's go and have Chinese class.

III. Pattern: <u>Qǐng gěi wǒ</u> yì bǎ chāzi.

Now finish the following:

1. Qǐng gěi wǒ _____.

2. Wǒ méiyǒu cānjīnzhǐ. Qǐng _____.

IV.   Pattern: Wǒ <u>bù</u> chī là de.   Wǒ <u>méi</u> chīguo yóutiáo.

Now fill in the blanks with "bù" or "méi":

1. Wǒ _____ chī zǎofàn yīnwèi wǒ bù xǐhuān chī zǎofàn.

2. Wǒ _____ hēguo Zhōngguó chá.

3. Xiǎo háizi dōu xǐhuān hē kělè, _____ xǐhuān hē chá.

4. Wǒ _____ qùguo Zhōngguó Chéng. Wǒ hěn xiǎng qù.

V.   Rewrite the following sentences by using " hǎo... a" :

1. Zhèi ge xuéxiào <u>dà jí le</u>.   2. Zhèi ge cài <u>tài là le</u>.

3. Nèi ge dàxué <u>zhème guì</u>.   4. Tā de qián <u>zhēn duō</u>.

Unit 6   Capsule 4

Communicative Tasks

Task 1:   Give responses to the statement:

A: Mápó Dòufu tài là le.

B: _____   _____

_____   _____

Task 2:   Now you have got a job working as a waiter/waitress in a Chinese restaurant in Chinatown.   You are required to speak Chinese to Chinese customers. Therefore, you are making a list of sentences and questions you will need to say. Complete the list before you go to the job.

Greeting customers at the table: _____!

Huānyíng_____!

Wǒ de míngzi_____.

Showing the menu: Qǐng_____.

Asking what they want to drink: Nǐmen_____?

Asking what they want to eat: Nǐmen_____?

Recommending special food: _____.

_____.

_____.

Putting the food on the table: Qǐng_____.

Asking if the food is good: _____?

Responding to "mǎi dān":   _____.

Saying "goodbye" to them: _____.

Pronunciation Drill

Practice saying the following tone combinations.

I.
```
------------------------------
      \      —
------------------------------
```

qìchē	(car)
xiàochē	(school bus)
diànchē	(trolley bus)
lǜ chē	(green car)
jiù chē	(used car)

II.
```
------------------------------------
        /      \
------------------------------------
```

yánsè	(color)
júsè	(orange color)
hóngsè	(red color)
lánsè	(blue color)
huángsè	(yellow color)

Listening Comprehension

Here are two listening tasks for you. Listen carefully and answer the questions in English.

Task 1

Question A: How many cars does this family own?

Question B: What are the colors of their cars?

Task 2

Question A: Where could this conversation have taken place?

Question B: Did the woman like the green car?

Question C: What color was the car the woman got at last?

Unit 7   Capsule 1

Structure Reinforcement

I.   Imagine you are a designer for all kinds of vehicles. Now in the first column, write
       down the kind of the vehicle you are designing, the second column the color(s) of that
       vehicle, and the third column the estimated price for that vehicle.

Vehicle	Color (s)	Price written in ...	
		numbers	pinyin
E.g. qìchē	bái	45,000.00	sìwàn wǔqiān kuài

II.   Follow the models given to describe the vehicles you have presented in the above chart:

       Models: Wǒde qìchē shì bái de.
                Wǒde qìchē yòu hǎo yòu kuài.
                Wǒde qìchē bǐ wǒ de zìxíngchē guì de duō. (or: guì yì diǎnr)

       _____

       _____

       _____

       _____

       _____

Communicative Tasks

Task 1:   Give responses to the statement given:

A: Tā de qìchē de yánsè shì zǐ sè de.

B: _____   _____

_____   _____

Task 2:   Answer the following questions according to your real situation.

1. Nǐ jiā yǒu jǐ liàng qìchē?

2. Nǐ bàba de qìchē shì shénme yánsè de?

3. Nǐ bàba de qìchē shì Měiguó qìchē háishì Rìběn qìchē?

4. Nǐ juéde nǐ māma de qìchē zěnmeyàng?

5. Nǐ yǒu méiyǒu qìchē?

6. Nǐ xiǎng yào yí liàng qìchē ma?

7. Nǐ xǐhuān shénme yánsè de qìchē?

8. Nǐ yǒu méiyǒu qián mǎi qìchē?

9. Nǐ jiā yǒu jǐ liàng zìxíngchē?

10. Nǐ juéde shénme zìxíngchē zuì hǎo?

11. Mótuōchē bǐ qìchē piányí ma?

12. Mótuōchē kuài háishì qìchē kuài?

13. Nǐmen xuéxiào de xiàochē shūfu ma?

14. Nǐ zhīdào bù zhīdào Běijīng yǒu méiyǒu dìtiě?

15. Nǐ zuòguo huǒchē ma?

Unit 7 Capsule 2

Pronunciation Drill

Practice saying the following tone combinations.

I.
```
--------------------------------
        ▬    ▬
--------------------------------
```

II.
```
--------------------------------------
              ＼    ∨
--------------------------------------
```

xīguā	(water melon)	dìtiě	(subway)
xiāngjiāo	(banana)	dàbǐng	(sesame seed cake)
kāfēi	(coffee)	guòjiǎng	(flatter)
xīnxiān	(fresh)	hàomǎ	(number)
hē tāng	(drink soup)	bù dǒng	(don't understand)

Listening Comprehension

Here are two listening tasks for you. Listen carefully and answer the questions in English.

Task 1

Question A: Name the fruits the person likes to eat.

_____

Question B: Which fruit doesn't he like? Why?

_____

Task 2

Question A: What fruit was the vendor selling?

_____

Question B: How was the vendor's fruit?

_____

Question C: What did people call the vendor?

_____

Structure Reinforcement

I. Design a fruit basket, which contains different kinds of fruit. Remember that each circle is for one kind of fruit. Label the name and color of each fruit you arrange for each circle.

Be sure to mix the colors well and not to put the water melon on top of grapes.

II. Write pinyin for the following according to the English given:

1. _____   2. _____   3. _____   4. _____
     (orange)   (pear)   (peach)   (plum)

5. _____   6. _____   7. _____   8. _____
      (cup)   (plate)   (fork)   (knife)

9. _____   10. _____   11. _____   12. __ érzi __
     (child)   (Confucius)   (Laozi)   (son)

All the above words have "zi." Can you make some kind of generalization for "zi"?

III. Pattern: Dàjiā dōu xǐhuān chī xīguā.

Now can you finish the following?

1. Dàjiā dōu xǐhuān hē _____.

2. Dàjiā dōu xiǎng mǎi _____.

3. Dàjiā _____ shuō _____.

4. Dàjiā _____ juéde _____.

Unit 7 Capsule 2

Communicative Tasks

Task 1:   Give responses to the statement given:

A: Wǒ bù xǐhuān chī píngguǒ.

B: _____   _____

_____   _____

Task 2:   You have learned the following words to describe how much you like something.

E.g.   hěn,   zuì,   yǒu yì diǎnr,   bǐjiào,   tèbié

Now students are telling how much they like learning Chinese. Please fill in the blanks with one of the words above and show how one feels stronger than another.

A: Wǒ xǐhuān xué Zhōngwén.
B: Wǒ _____ xǐhuān xué Zhōngwén.
C: Wǒ _____ xǐhuān xué Zhōngwén.
D: Wǒ _____ xǐhuān xué Zhōngwén.
E: Wǒ _____ xǐhuān xué Zhōngwén.
F: Wǒ _____ xǐhuān xué Zhōngwén.

Task 3:   You have learned the following ways to describe something:

zhēn ...,   zhème ...,   bú gòu ...,   tài ... le,   bǐjiào ...,
tèbié ...,   ..., kěshì...,   ..., yě ...,   yòu ... yòu ...,   yǒu yìdiǎnr ...

Now make comments on the fruits in the fruit basket on the previous page. You may give both positive or negative comments on different fruits.

positive comments   negative comments

_____   _____

_____   _____

_____   _____

_____   _____

Pronunciation Drill

Practice saying the following tone combinations.

I.

pǐxié   (dress shoes)
míngpái   (brand name)
shímáo   (fashionable)
pútáo   (grape)
piányí   (inexpensive)

II.

dà hào   (large size)
yùndòng   (sports)
wàitào   (outer garment)
diànhuà   (telephone)
dòngwù   (animal)

Listening Comprehension

Here are two listening tasks for you. Listen carefully and answer the questions in English.

Task 1

Question A: Did the woman buy the red sweater? Why?

_____

Question B: Did the woman buy the blue sweater? Why?

_____

Task 2

Question A: What did the man want to buy?

_____

Question B: Did he buy what he was looking for? Why?

_____

Structure Reinforcement

I.　You will go to Beijing for a 3-month trip in the fall (September to November). Make a list of clothes you plan to bring. Specify the color of clothes, and also the quantity of each kind of clothes. See the model.

quantity	color	item	quantity	color	item
yí jiàn	hóng	wàitào	wǔ jiàn	bái	hànshān

II.　Write opposites of the following words that can be used to describe clothes or shoes. Also write the English meaning as shown in the model.

dà --- xiǎo　　　　　cháng ---　　　　　guì ---
(big)　(small)　　　　(　　)　(　　)　　　(　　)　(　　)

hǎokàn ---　　　　　shūfu ---　　　　　shímáo ---
(　　)　(　　)　　　(　　)　(　　)　　　(　　)　(　　)

III.　Fill in the blanks with correct question words so that the following will make sense.

1.　Zhèi jiàn dàyī _____? Yìbǎi kuài.

2.　Nǐ yào mǎi _____ hànshān? Liǎng jiàn.

3.　Nǐ yào mǎi _____ niúzǎikù? Zhèi tiáo.

4.　Nǐ chuān _____ de xiézi? Jiǔ hào.

Communicative Tasks

Task 1:   Give responses to the statement:

A: Wǒ xǐhuān chuān niúzǎikù.

B: _____   _____

   _____   _____

Task 2:   Now you are going to buy clothes in Chinatown. Many shop assistants (SA) there speak very limited English. Besides, you want to practice your Chinese. Therefore, you are making a list of sentences and questions that you will hear or you will need to say while shopping in Chinatown. Complete the list before you go there.

I tell the SA that I want a Chinese T-shirt.	Wǒ xiǎng_____. Nǐmen yǒu _____?
The SA asks me what color of the T-shirt I want.	Nǐ yào_____?
I ask the SA if they have red ones.	Nǐmen _____?
I ask the SA if they have bigger ones.	Yǒu méiyǒu_____?
The SA asks about my size.	Nǐ chuān_____?
I tell the SA that I wear Large.	Wǒ chuān_____.
I make negative comments on the T-shirt.	Zhèi jiàn_____. Zhèi jiàn_____.
I make a positive comment on the T-shirt.	Zhèi jiàn_____.
I ask about the price.	Zhèi jiàn_____?
I want to try on....	Ràng_____.
I want to buy this T-shirt.	Wǒ yào_____.

Unit 7　Capsule 4

Pronunciation Drill

Practice saying the following tone combinations.

I.

V ／

dǎzhé	(discount)
cǎoméi	(strawberry)
yǒumíng	(famous)
xiǎohái	(children)
hǎorén	(good person)

II.

＼ ／

zìyóu	(free)
tèbié	(especially)
qùnián	(last year)
bù xíng	(not OK)
wèntí	(problem)

Listening Comprehension

Here are two listening tasks for you. Listen carefully and answer the questions in English.

Task 1

Question A:　What was the initial discount ?

_____

Question B:　What was the final discount ?

_____

Question C:　How did the customer bargain for such a good discount?

_____

Task 2

Question A:　Where did they decide to go shopping?

_____

Question B:　Why didn't they want to shop at the free market?

_____

I.   Expanding sentences:

      Wǒ _____ cài shìchǎng. (I go to the food market.)

      Wǒ māma _____ wǒ yìqǐ _____ cài shìchǎng.
      (My mom and I go to the food market together.)

      Wǒ māma _____ wǒ _____ ____ cài shìchǎng _____.
      (My mom and I go to the food market together to do some shopping.)

II.   Let's make comparison.

      Tom _____ John gāo.
      Eric bǐ Bill _____ de duō.

      Bill bǐ Tom _____ yì diǎnr.
      Eric zuì _____. John _____ ǎi.

III.   Finish the following sentences:

    1. Zhèr yǒu _____. (There are many schools here.)

    2. _____ yǒu _____ ma? (Is there an elementary school here?)

    3. Nàr yǒu _____. (There's a restaurant over there.)

    4. _____ yí ge zìyóu shìchǎng? (Where is there a free market?)

IV.   "Dōngxī" is an interesting word. By itself, "dōng" means "east," and "xī" means "west."
      However, when they are put together, "dōngxī" means "stuff, thing, things."
      Finish the combinations with "dōngxī" according to the English meaning given:

    1. _____ dōngxī   2. _____ dōngxī
        (this)   (that)

    3. _____ dōngxī   4. _____ dōngxī
        (my)   (whose)

    5. _____ dōngxī   6. _____ dōngxī
        (many)   (very good)

    7. zhèr de _____   8. _____ dōngxī
        (things here)   (things there)

Communicative Tasks

Task 1:   Give responses to the statement:

A: Mǎi yī sòng yī.

B: _____   _____

_____   _____

Task 2:   Let's prepare for the "Classroom Market" by summarizing what we can say as a buyer and a seller.

As a seller		As a buyer	
Asking customers to come and buy.	Kuài _____! Wǒ de _____ yòu ___ yòu ___.	Asking about the price.	_____ duōshao qián? _____ yí jiàn ?
Telling customers that prices are reduced.	Dǎ _____! Dǎ _____! Duō mǎi _____!	Making negative comments.	_____ bú gòu _____! _____ zhème _____! _____ tài _____!
Telling the prices.	_____ yí jiàn. Liǎng jiàn _____. _____, nǐ yào bú yào?	Asking if there is a bigger /red / better/less expensive one.	Yǒu méiyǒu _____de? Yǒu méiyǒu _____de? Yǒu méiyǒu _____de? Yǒu méiyǒu _____de?
Telling how good your products are.	_____ _____ _____ _____	Making comparison of the products.	_____ bǐ _____. _____ bǐ _____ ___ de duō. _____ bǐ _____ ___ yì diǎnr. _____ zuì _____.
Asking which one the customer wants.	_____ něi yí jiàn? Nǐ yào _____ háishì _____?	Bargaining the price.	_____ nǐ mài bú mài? _____ xíng bù xíng?
(Dis)agreeing with the price offered.	Hǎo. Xíng. (Bù xíng.)	Telling that you want to buy ….	Hǎo, wǒ _____.

Pronunciation Drill

Practice saying the following tone combinations.

I.

```
-------------------------------
         \    —
-------------------------------
```

II.

```
-------------------------------
              —r
-------------------------------
```

Yàzhōu	(Asia)		zhèr	(here)
diànchē	(trolley)		nàr	(there)
dàjiā	(everyone)		nǎr	(where)
chènshān	(shirt)		yì diǎnr	(a little)

Listening Comprehension

Here are two listening tasks for you. Listen carefully and answer the questions in English.

Task 1

Question A: Did they go to Beijing Restaurant? Why?

_____

Question B: Which restaurant did they decide to go? Why?

_____

Task 2

Question A: Where is Xiao Wang from?

_____

Question B: Where is Taiwan?

_____

Question B: Has John been to Taiwan?

_____

Unit 8   Capsule 1

Structure Reinforcement

I.   Fill in the blanks with one of the following question words:

> něi guó rén   něi yì nián   něi yì tiān
> něi ge lǎoshī   něi běn shū   něi zhī bǐ   nǎr

1. Nǐ shì _____?   2. Nǐ yào kàn _____?

3. Nǐ shì _____ shēng de?   4. _____ shì nǐ de?

5. Nǐmen _____ qù Niǔyuē?   6. Nǐ de xuéxiào zài _____?

7. _____ shì nǐ de Zhōngwén lǎoshī?

II.   Patterns: Nǐ jiā <u>zài nǎr</u>?   Nǐ jiā <u>zài</u> ... <u>ma</u>?

What should you say if you want to ask ...?

1. Where is Xiao Li's home?

2. Where is your brother's college?

3. Is Beijing University in Beijing?

III.   Patterns: Běijīng lí Shànghǎi hěn yuǎn.

Finish the following according to the English given:

1. Wǒ jiā _____ xuéxiào _____. (My home is very close to the school.)

2. Wáng Lǎoshī de jiā _____ hěn yuǎn.
   (Teacher Wang's home is far from the school.)

3. _____ lí zhèr hěn jìn? (Whose home is near here?)

4. _____ dàxué _____ Niǔyuē hěn jìn? (Which university is near New York?)

5. Wǒ jiā lí Shànghǎi Dàxué _____, yě _____.
   (My home is not near, nor close to Shanghai University.)

Communicative Tasks

Task 1:   Give responses to the statement:

A: Wǒ jiā lí zhèr bù yuǎn.

B: _____   _____

_____   _____

Task 2:   Ma Daming is now in Taipei. He wants to find a big street market. Help Daming to finish the following dialogue with an old man in the street:

Ma: Lǎo _____, qǐng _____, zhèr _____ chāojí _____ ma?

Man: Yǒu a! Yǒu liǎng ge.

Ma: Liǎng _____ chāojí shìchǎng dōu hěn _____ ma?

Man: Bù, yí ge dà, yí ge xiǎo!

Ma: Něi _____ jìn?

Man: Dà de chāojí shìchǎng bǐ xiǎo de yuǎn yì diǎnr.

Ma: Xiǎo _____ chāojí shìchǎng _____?

Man: Hěn bú cuò! Yǒu hěnduō dōngxī.

Ma: _____ nǐ, lǎo bóbo! _____!

Man: Zàijiàn!

Task 3:   Write several sentences about Shanghai.
(Hints: big, famous, far from..., near ..., many people, street markets, clothing.
Try to use: zuì, zhēn, ...jí le, yě, yòu...yòu..., kěshì ...)

_____

_____

_____

_____

_____

Unit 8   Capsule 2

Pronunciation Drill

Practice saying the following tone combinations.

I.

╱   ╲

----

chídào	(be late)
chángkù	(long pants)
huódòng	(activity)
Táibì	(Taiwan money)

II.

...+diǎn

----

sān diǎn	(3:00)
shí diǎn	(10:00)
sì diǎn	(4:00)
wǔ diǎn	(5:00)

Listening Comprehension

Here are two listening tasks for you. Listen carefully and answer the questions in English.

Task 1

Question A: Where do they plan to go?

_____

Question B: When and where will they meet each other?

_____

Task 2

Question A: What time should the school bus come?

_____

Question B: Did Xiao Wang miss his school bus?

_____

Question C: What time is it now?

_____

Structure Reinforcement

I.   Use the table to learn how to write the following time in pinyin:

time	year	month	date	day	a.m./p.m.	time of clock
4:30 p.m. May 7, 1996 (Tuesday)	yī jiǔ jiǔ liù nián	wǔyuè	qī rì	xīngqī èr	xiàwǔ	sì diǎn bàn
7:15 a.m. March 30, 1997 (Sunday)						
11:05 a.m. February 16 (Friday)						
6:45 p.m. June 26, 1997 (Thursday)						
10:10 p.m. October 23						
2:30 p.m., next Wednesday						

II.   Use the pattern: "Wǒ kěyǐ bù kěyǐ ... ?" to ask your teacher for the permission to ... :

1. go and drink water

2. write characters now

3. go to the bathroom (cèsuǒ)

III.   Use the pattern: "Nǐ kěyǐ jiāo wǒ ... ma?" to ask someone to ... :

1. teach you martial arts

2. teach you Chinese dance

IV.   Use the pattern: "Nǐ shénme shíhòu kěyǐ ... ?" to ask your friend when he/she can ...:

1. teach you to do Chinese painting

2. go back home

Unit 8   Capsule 2

Communicative Tasks

Task 1:   Give responses to the statement given:

A: Jīntiān wǎnshang qī diǎn jiàn, xíng ma?

B: _____   _____

_____   _____

Task 2:   You are trying to ask your friend to go to Xiao Wang's home. But he is too busy
to find the time. Finish the following dialogue.
(Hints: Use "..., hǎo bùhǎo?" "..., xíng bù xíng?" "... zěnmeyàng?")

--- Wǒmen _____ qù Xiǎo Wáng jiā hǎo ma?

--- Bù xíng. Wǒ míngtiān xiàwǔ yào qù xué tiàowǔ.

--- _____?

--- Duìbuqǐ. Wǒ měi xīngqī sān xiàwǔ yǒu chànggē kè.

--- _____?

--- Kěshì wǒ māma shuō wǒ wǎnshang bù kěyǐ chūqù (go out).

--- Āiyā, āiyā !

Task 3:   Finish the following dialogue according to the English meaning given:

--- _____. (See you tomorrow.)

--- Míngtiān shénme shíhòu jiàn?

--- _____. (See you tomorrow afternoon.)

--- Xiàwǔ shénme shíhòu jiàn?

--- _____. (See you at 3:00 p.m. tomorrow.)

--- Zài nǎr jiàn?

--- _____.

(See you at Xiao Wang's home at 3:00 p.m. tomorrow afternoon.)

Pronunciation Drill

Practice saying the following tone combinations.

I. -----------------------------------   II.   ---

           ＼ + ...   ∨ + ...

           -----------------------------------   ---

shàngkè	(have lessons)	jǐ diǎn	(what time)
xiàkè	(finish class)	jǐ wèi	(how many guests)
shàngwǔ	(before noon)	jǐ liàng	(how many cars)
xiàwǔ	(afternoon)	jǐ hào	(what size/what number)
shàngxué	(go to school)	jǐ yuè jǐ hào	(what date)
fàngxué	(finish classes)	jǐ ge	(how many)

Listening Comprehension

Here are two listening tasks for you. Listen carefully and answer the questions in English.

Task 1

     Question A: What is Wang Wei's morning schedule?

                    _____

     Question B: When and how does Wang Wei come home from school?

                    _____

Task 2

     Question A: What does Xiao Wang do every evening?

                    _____

     Question B: What does Xiao Wang think about learning Chinese?

                    _____

Unit 8 Capsule 3

I.   Study the word order of the following building blocks for the sentence.

Can you make sentences to tell that at certain time you do certain things?

_____

_____

_____

_____

II.   Now when the specific time of the clock is missing, what should we say to ask a question?

Can you make questions to ask someone at what time he/she does certain things?

_____

_____

_____

_____

III.   Complete the following questions by using "zěnme":

   1. Nǐmen míngtiān _____? (how to go to New York)

   2. Wáng Lǎoshī, zhèi ge zì _____? (how to write)

   3. Wáng Lǎoshī, Zhōngwén _____ "sports"? (how to say)

Communicative Tasks

Task 1:   Give responses to the statement:

A: Wǒ zǎoshang zǒulù qù xuéxiào.

B: _____   _____

_____   _____

Task 2:   Tell about what you do every day:

1. Wǒ měi tiān dōu _____.

2. Wǒ _____.

3. Wǒ _____.

Task 3:   Answer the following questions according to your real situation.

1. Nǐ měi tiān shénme shíhòu qǐchuáng?

2. Nǐ zǎoshang shénme shíhòu qù xuéxiào?

3. Nǐ zài nǎr niànshū?

4. Nǐ zěnme qù xuéxiào?

5. Nǐ jiā lí xuéxiào jìn ma?

6. Nǐ měi tiān shénme shíhòu fàngxué?

7. Nǐ měi tiān dōu yùndòng ma?

8. Nǐ xiàwǔ yùndòng háishì wǎnshang yùndòng?

9. Nǐ shénme shíhòu zuò gōngkè?

10. Nǐ měi tiān dōu yǒu hěnduō gōngkè ma?

11. Nǐ shénme shíhòu shuìjiào?

Unit 8   Capsule 4

Pronunciation Drill

Practice saying the following tone combinations.

I. -------------------------------
\ \

II. -------------------------------
/ /

shuìjiào	(sleep)	lánqiú	(basketball)
kèqì	(be polite)	zúqiú	(soccer)
diànshì	(TV)	chángcháng	(often)
diàndòng	(video game)	Chángchéng	(the Great Wall)
diànhuà	(telephone)	tóngxué	(classmate)

Task 1

Question A: What does Wang Wei like to do?

_____

Question B: How about his friend?

_____

Task 2

Question A: What will the two friends do tonight?

_____

Question B: What kind of sports can Xiao Wang do?

_____

Structure Reinforcement

I.   You have learned the following words to tell how often you do certain things:
    měi tiān,   tiāntiān,   chángcháng,
    hěnshǎo,   yǒu shíhòu,   měi xīngqī tiān

Now students are talking about how often they practice Chinese calligraphy. Fill in the blanks to show how the frequency increases one by one. Then write the English meaning.

A: Wǒ bù xiě máobǐ zì.   (I do not practice Chinese calligraphy.)

B: Wǒ _____ xiě máobǐ zì. (   )

C: Wǒ _____ xiě máobǐ zì. (   )

D: Wǒ _____ xiě máobǐ zì. (   )

E: Wǒ _____ xiě máobǐ zì. (   )

F: Wǒ _____ xiě máobǐ zì. (   )

G: Wǒ _____ xiě máobǐ zì. (   )

II.   Pattern: Wǒ tiàowǔ tiào de hěn hǎo.

Now try to describe someone's swimming skills in many different ways:

1. Tā yóuyǒng yóu de _____.

2. Tā yóuyǒng yóu de _____.

3. Tā yóuyǒng _____.

4. Tā yóuyǒng _____.

5. Tā _____.

6. Tā _____.

III.   Patterns: Wǒ tīngshuō nàr de dōngxī hěn piányí.

        Wǒ juéde tā chàng de búcuò.

Now finish the following:

1. Wǒ tīngshuō _____.

2. Wǒ juéde _____.

3. Nǐ juéde _____ zěnmeyàng?

4. Nǐ juéde _____ háishì _____?

Unit 8   Capsule 4

Communicative Tasks

Task 1:   Give responses to the statement:

A: Wǒ juéde tā chànggē chàng de hěn zāogāo.

B: _____   _____

_____   _____

Task 2:   Answer the following questions according to your real situation.

1.   Nǐ měi tiān dōu kàn diànshì ma?

2.   Nǐ juéde měi tiān kàn diànshì hǎo bù hǎo? Wèi shénme?

3.   Shéi huì huáxuě? Nǐ juéde tā huá de zěnmeyàng?

4.   Nǐ xǐhuān pǎobù ma?

5.   Nǐ tiāntiān dōu pǎobù ma?

6.   Nǐ pǎo de kuài bú kuài?

7.   Nǐ zuì xǐhuān shénme yùndòng?

8.   Nǐ xǐhuān dǎ shénme qiú?

9.   Nǐ xǐhuān dǎ lánqiú háishì dǎ bàngqiú?

10.   Nǐ juéde tī gǎnlǎnqiú zěnmeyàng?

11.   Nǐ chángcháng qù kàn diànyǐng ma?

12.   Nǐ chángcháng hé shéi yìqǐ qù kàn diànyǐng?

13.   Shéi xiě Zhōngguó zì xiě de bǐ nǐ kuài?

14.   Shéi bǐ nǐ yóuyǒng yóu de kuài?

15.   Nǐ xiǎngxué yóuyǒng ma?